M M Hewson
1976.

LOS ANGELES COUNTY MUSEUM OF ART

NOCTURNE. 1963

GERTRUD AND OTTO NATZLER

Ceramics

Catalog of the Collection of

MRS. LEONARD M. SPERRY

and a Monograph by Otto Natzler

LOS ANGELES COUNTY MUSEUM OF ART

1968

PHOTOGRAPHY BY MAX YAVNO

Thirty-five hundred copies of this book have been
printed at the Plantin Press, Los Angeles.

FOREWORD

WHEN I FIRST SAW the work of Gertrud and Otto Natzler, I recalled the phrase which Giorgio Vasari used in 1550, to characterize the Villa Farnesina in Rome "…not built, but actually born…" For those pots in their subtle but infinite variety of simple, unaffected shapes and surfaces seemed to have been born and to have grown as if they were natural things. I was not surprised, therefore, to hear Otto make a similar comment while watching Gertrud work. For this is the essence of the Natzlers' philosophy of art and way of life. They live in communion with the trees and thick planting surrounding their house and the natural textures of wood, wool and linen inside it. Their studio is small, devoid of gadgets and complex machinery. They work in close association, collaborating on every piece, each doing what his natural talents indicate: Gertrud at the wheel; Otto at the kiln.

In shaping a pot, Gertrud does not work like the Renaissance artist, about whom Vasari wrote, who learned the laws of nature and imposed them rationally upon his material; the wheel is far too fast for that. She is rather like a musical virtuoso who lets the form flow intuitively from her fingers. The resultant shapes seem timeless, recalling now 17th century Japan, now 10th century Persia or wherever the artist restrained his highly trained hands to produce a refined, natural simplicity.

Through years of experiment and discovery, Otto has developed glazes as fine as insect wings and rough as cratered lava. He works, however, with a consciousness of the limitations of human invention and in the final firing allows nature to give each piece its unique color and texture. In this manner, he produces the perfect complement to Gertrud's shapes, at the same time original and normative.

The Natzlers and the Los Angeles County Museum of Art have found an extraordinary patron in Mrs. Leonard Sperry. Over the years she has formed a retrospective collection which indicates both the scope and variety of the Natzler work in America. She has now provided for the publication of this book so that she can share her own joy in the collection with readers everywhere, and she has further bequeathed the collection to the Los Angeles County Museum of Art so that it will eventually become part of the heritage of California.

I would like to express to Mrs. Sperry my own gratitude and the deep appreciation of the Board of Trustees and staff of the Museum.

KENNETH DONAHUE, Director
Los Angeles County Museum of Art

PREFACE

I met Gertrud and Otto Natzler in the early 1950's. On that occasion, I told them that I had been aware of their work for some time and had acquired several of their ceramics which had given me great pleasure.

A few weeks later, my husband and I visited the Natzlers at their studio. He suggested that I select a piece as a birthday gift from him. Without foreknowledge it now appears that I chose a very unusual pot — the very first of what was later to become my "historical collection."

I cannot pinpoint the exact date on which the idea of a chronological collection came to me, but ultimately I knew that I wanted to have a retrospective collection of Natzler ceramics dating from the first years of their work in the United States. As I thought this through, it became clear to me that one day I should present this collection in toto to a leading museum in order that many more people than my intimate group of friends could enjoy it.

I found it very difficult to acquire any early pieces and so the Natzlers were gracious enough to arrange that I should own, from their personal collection, fine examples from the years 1940 to 1945. Their availability being so limited, I do not take credit for selecting these pots as my own choice. Coming from their collection, they reflect what the Natzlers felt were significant examples of that particular period. The pots from later years were acquired from a much larger spectrum, frequently at Kiln Openings.

The reason for this catalog, I am sure, is quite obvious. There should be in existence a definitive work on the accomplishments of these artists through the years, and so I have prevailed on Otto Natzler to write the text for this book. Since I love my pots and they have become an important part of my life, I wish to share my pleasure with others.

ROSE A. SPERRY

INTRODUCTION

THIS BOOK is intended primarily to be a complete catalog of the collection of Natzler Ceramics assembled over the years by Mrs. Leonard M. Sperry.

The accompanying monograph contains part of an autobiography, relating to our earliest working period, as I believe that these years strongly affected our thinking and outlook. Its inclusion in this book also serves as a substitute for the impressive list of colleges, art schools, individual teachers and masters most artists can provide as their background and we cannot. We were not influenced in our work by schools, teachers or movements. As far as ceramics go, we were largely self-taught. The book further includes heretofore unpublished material on our Clay and Glazes, on Form and Gertrud's Throwing, which may shed light on our philosophy and attitudes toward our medium.

This is a very personal document, not attempting in any way to be objective, but on the contrary expressing views on our work in a most subjective manner. It illustrates how for me it was a simple matter of "cherchez-la-femme," and happily accepting all that was connected with one "femme" in particular, for at the time I met Gertrud, nothing was farther from my mind than clay. What developed was a life together, dedicated to the work we love.

We have always maintained that an artist should be judged by his work and not by what he has to say about it. In writing the text for this catalog I do not mean to contradict this conviction, but rather hope to provide the viewer of our ceramics with some knowledge about the human beings behind the work and how the work itself came to be.

OTTO NATZLER

Santa Barbara, California
Summer 1967

ACKNOWLEDGMENTS

Above all I should like to express our grateful appreciation for the sustained interest Mrs. Leonard M. Sperry and her late husband have shown in our work. Our relationship with the Sperrys became far more than that of an artist to his collector. Over the years a deep-rooted friendship developed of which the assembling of this collection was but a small part.

Thanks are due Charles F. Haas for the unstinting help he has given me by reading the manuscript and final proofs, to Bess Kaufman and Helen Raizen for their valuable comments, to Max Yavno for his superb photography and complete devotion to a difficult task, to Saul and Lillian Marks of the Plantin Press for designing and printing the book, and last, but not least, I thank Gertrud, my wife, for her editorial help and unwavering support throughout.

O. N.

GREY CELADON TEARDROP BOTTLE.   1961

THE BEGINNING OF IT ALL

The years 1933-1938 in Vienna

[I]

LIKE SO MANY of life's most important happenings, the beginning
was purely accidental. And God knows, had it not rained in Vienna
on Sunday, the 30th of July 1933, Gertrud and I might never have
come to know each other and both our lives might have taken off in
completely different directions.

I had known her brother, Hans Amon, for several years. He owned
a bookstore that was located in the building where I then lived. His
bookstore was one of those, typical of Vienna, where one went, not
always to buy books, but sometimes just to browse, meet people and
talk, and I was in the habit of dropping in fairly frequently. Though
Hella, Hans's wife, had often mentioned Gertrud, I had never seen her.
As it happened, I met her at the store on Friday before *that* Sunday. It
was a rather casual introduction; she had come by at just about closing
time. Hans and I were supposed to go out together that evening and he
said he would come up to my apartment after a while. When he arrived,
Gertrud was still with him. They came in for a few minutes and Gertrud's eye fell on a ceramic vase from the Wiener Werkstätte that someone had given me. She looked at it and asked Hans whether he liked it.
I thought it strange that she should single out this one object, as I had

never paid any particular attention to it before. We all left shortly, and as we went down the stairs, Gertrud mentioned to her brother that she intended to go to the Danube with some friends next Sunday. Only in case of rain would she come out to their parents' summer house in the Hinterbrühl. Our ways parted when we got to the street.

I had a long-standing invitation from Hans to visit at this house one weekend, an invitation I had never accepted. That evening I told him that I might want to come out on Sunday. Though I had hardly exchanged a word with Gertrud, I was terribly interested in seeing her again. I prayed for rain that Sunday and rain it did.

To get to the Hinterbrühl from Vienna—a distance of hardly more than twelve miles—was quite an undertaking. First one had to take the streetcar to go to the Südbahnhof, from there one took the train to Mödling and then one changed to a little old rickety electric train that took one to the Hinterbrühl. That last part of the trip was most delightful, as the train went through beautifully scenic and romantic country. It started out rather drably at the railroad station in Mödling, went through the small town and, once out of it, continued toward its destination squeezing itself by big boulders, past running springs with beautiful ferns, past trees and lush meadows. The train hobbled slowly on its rather worn-out tracks, there were many stops on its short run, and one could really see and enjoy the landscape through its windows. Whenever I could, I loved to sit on the open rear platform of the last car, looking back on the tracks as the train passed through the intimate terrain.

The whole trip took about two hours, that is if one was lucky and made good connections, and considerably longer if one was not. On

GREY "CRATER" BOTTLE. 1960

account of the rain – and what a beautiful rain it was – the trains were not crowded and the ride was fairly comfortable for a Sunday in mid-summer. The last part of the ride was especially enjoyable, as the rain had made everything even greener and more lush than usual.

I arrived at the house in the Hinterbrühl slightly wet from the last half-mile walk from the station, and completely unexpected. I had never come when the weather was beautiful, why should I have come in this miserable rain!? I had my reasons, even though no one else knew about them. To my great disappointment, the main reason for my coming was entirely out of sight.

I finally inquired about Gertrud, whether she was there at all, or whether she had perhaps changed her mind about coming. Yes, she was there, still sound asleep, having been out late the night before. What else was there to do in such miserable weather? But then Senta, Hans's little daughter, went to awaken her.

At last she appeared, sleepy, half-surprised and half-annoyed that somebody, some friend of her brother's, should have inquired about her and had her awakened. What a rain!

We had settled on a covered veranda facing the garden, the rain still falling gently and interminably and – of all things – had started to play a game of poker. Something impelled me to induce Gertrud to gamble. I don't remember anything about the game, I don't know who won or who lost. I know that I watched only her and when the game was over, I stayed on and we all had supper with her family. After nightfall Gertrud and I went back to Vienna together.

Going home from the Vienna Woods on a Sunday night, the trains were crowded. It had finally stopped raining and we both sat on the

4

PEACHBLOOM BOTTLE. 1955

EMERALD-SILVERBLACK BOTTLE. 1965

steps of the railroad car on the open platform, going through the dark landscape, the monotonous thumping of the wheels under us.

The trip was terribly short. What had taken such a long two hours in the morning, took such a short two hours at night. I don't remember too much of what we talked about. But among many things we discussed, Gertrud mentioned that she had just recently started to work with clay and found it such a fascinating material. One made ceramics from it.

The word "clay" intrigued me. The German word for it is "Ton," the same word as a tone in music. I had always loved music and for a time I wanted to be a musician. I had played the violin ever since I was seven and when I met Gertrud, I was studying seriously, practicing five to six hours a day. The word "Ton" itself offered a pleasant association.

The word "ceramics" made me shudder. For some reason I did not relate clay with ceramics. In fact, ceramics to me meant all those cute little multi-colored figurines, vases and compotes with appliquéd flowers, birds or fruit, plates and dishes decorated with leaves or insects, clowns or mermaids or, at best, the stuff that came out of the Wiener Werkstätte—"Angewandte Kunst" (applied art)—where the little painted animal figures could be *used* to stamp out a cigaret in a matching ashtray. These were the ceramics I knew. I found them rather meaningless, quite distressing.

I did not say this to Gertrud. On the contrary, on parting that evening, I found it convenient to ask her to bring me some clay. For some reason I was too shy to ask her for a date outright, and so I used this devious way to see her again.

Indeed, three days later she brought me the clay, a big lump of wet

5

clay, weighing perhaps twenty pounds; she could hardly carry it. She gave it to me as a gift, together with some "pointers" as to how it should be handled. Little did I realize that she herself did not know much about it, having started to dabble in clay just a few weeks before. But she was so enthusiastic, and all I knew was that I had fallen in love with her.

I took the clay home and told Gertrud that she would have to see what I would do with it. Two days later I called her. I wanted to show her my first two "masterworks," a sketchy figure of a man and a mask of Bronislaw Huberman, the distinguished violinist whom I adored and whose likeness I had tried to reconstruct from memory. Though both pieces were very bad, as I realized later, Gertrud seemed impressed. She wanted to show them to her teacher and hear his opinion. I had no objections, at least this would provide another occasion for us to meet. A few days later she called to tell me that her teacher had found both pieces "very interesting." Not only that, but on learning that they were the first attempts of someone who had never touched clay before, he did not fail to impress upon her that here was a talent that should be developed. He did not say preferably by him, but he did tell Gertrud that he would like to meet me.

Gertrud was truly impressed and said so. I was partly surprised, partly flattered and did not quite know what to think. I had not expected this. After all, I had now reached the ripe age of twenty-five without ever having thought of clay or sculpting, except perhaps at age four or five when I played with something called "Plastilin." Just a few weeks earlier I had lost my job as a textile designer, a job I had held for over five years and which I had hated. I had nothing else to do, I had all the time in the world. What did I have to lose? Would she introduce me

6

PALE YELLOW BOWL. 1952

to her teacher? Of course she would. "It takes nearly an hour to get there." "Never mind, you are going with me, aren't you?" "Yes, we can go next Saturday when I have my lesson."

That was all I needed. I was delighted with the way everything developed. It was obvious that my main interest was Gertrud, the clay was incidental, quite secondary, though interesting. By this time I had forgotten about "ceramics."

I could hardly wait until Saturday. Gertrud had asked me to meet her at noon outside the office where she worked. She had a full-time job as a secretary, a job she thoroughly disliked. To spend the whole day taking dictation, only to deposit a heap of letters in the corner mail box at night, seemed so futile. She had always wanted to do something with her hands, even if it was just making pots to plant flowers in.

We walked to a nearby restaurant to have a light lunch and afterwards we took the long ride on the streetcar together to get to her teacher.

7

THE WORKSHOP of Franz Iskra was in an old building at the outskirts of Vienna. You entered from the street through a small side door, walked about eight or ten steps down a wooden staircase, and there you were. It was a rather cramped workshop. The few small windows, starting at above eye level and reaching to the low ceiling, did not provide much illumination. They faced out onto the street and through them one could observe the lower portion of the legs of any passers-by.

It was early afternoon when we arrived and the room had a dark and musty appearance on entering it from the outside. After a while my eyes got accustomed to the dim light and I could discern the various objects and persons in the room.

It was filled with pots and more pots, with sculptures in all stages— some were covered with wet rags and quite mysterious looking—and empty armatures looking like skeletons. There were three old potter's wheels on one side of the room which was crammed with tables and benches. The door to an adjoining room was open, revealing a fairly large kiln, and approaching it, I could feel the warm air coming toward me. Seven or eight students of varying ages were busily occupied with whatever they were doing at the moment, completely absorbed in their work and paying no attention to anyone.

I had never been in a ceramic workshop before and the atmosphere of the place intrigued me. The dim light coming through the small windows undoubtedly helped, placing everything and everyone in an unreal half-light.

In contrast to his students' rather motionless absorption, Mr. Iskra himself was busily running back and forth, accompanied by an assistant, setting up shelves and pedestals for an "exhibition." He, too, was completely engrossed in what he was doing and paid no attention to anyone entering the place. Gertrud finally managed to introduce me. He was a man of medium build, in his mid-forties, bald-headed with slightly greying hair at the temples, and a somewhat mischievous expression in his grey-blue eyes when he smiled. He apologized for being so rushed, "but the preparations for this exhibition"…He did not finish the sentence. His voice was melodic, it had that peculiar rhythm of ending each sentence on an upbeat, as if asking a question. He spoke in a strong Viennese dialect, but quite pleasantly so. He mentioned my two "great" works and asked whether I really had never worked in clay before. His tone of voice seemed to imply that he could hardly believe it. He soon excused himself and said to make myself at home, and watch and inform myself about anything that interested me. He would be with me later.

In the meantime Gertrud had changed clothes, and put on a blue apron spattered with dried clay. She had sat down at one of the wheels and started to wedge clay. She looked beautiful, the faded blue of the apron complementing her olive complexion, and so "professional" at the same time. I stood there watching her. The wedging went on in a monotonous rhythm for some time, when suddenly she threw a lump of clay on the wheel-head. The sharp clap startled me. She started to kick the flywheel with her feet, setting it in rotating motion, and began somewhat awkwardly to center the clay. After a little while this formless lump became completely round, and slowly digging in with her

9

fingers and bending her head over to the side to look at the profile of the rotating clay, she pulled it up with both hands. There, in hardly a minute or two was what looked like a small pot, and it seemed miraculous how it had come into being. I must have stood there with my mouth open, for she noticed my amazement and tried to explain what she had done. But I just looked at her, I did not understand, and I guess she was not too good at explaining it either.

There is something very fascinating about wet clay and seeing it formed by skilled hands. Gertrud's hands were not yet very skilled, but they were immensely expressive, even though she labored a little too much and was still quite unsure as to the results.

She took a wire, cut the pot off at the base, and carefully lifted it off the wheel. Then she put it on a board next to her. "I have to work on it again…at the base…after it has dried somewhat," she said; and again I did not understand what she meant. She began to wedge clay once more and to form another pot. It seemed to go easier this time, and while working she tried again to explain to me what she was doing. To see the clay "grow" and take on form as you watch, even if it is not the most perfect form, seems like a miracle, and I looked on in complete fascination.

After a while Gertrud interrupted her work and showed me around the workshop. She explained to me that the clay has to dry completely before it can be fired in the kiln. After the firing the clay is hard; at this stage the glaze can be applied, and she showed me how this is done, too. There, on a bench, were several glass jars filled with various liquids, some white, some grey, pink or orange. She took a pink one, shook it and poured some of the liquid in a container. She then painted a small

BLUE CRYSTALLINE VASE. 1960

terracotta bowl by stippling the pink liquid on it with a paint brush. It seemed to dry almost instantly.

"This is a green glaze," she said expertly, in a matter-of-fact tone.

"Green did you say?! It looks very pink to me."

"Yes, I guess I should have said, it will be green after it is fired."

"I have to believe you, but how come? What makes it so?"

"I don't know, it just will be green. It says so here on the label, and I know. The pink here, for instance, is blue. This grey is black. *This* grey is yellow." She pointed to different jars. It did say so on the labels.

I was fascinated. Even though she could not give me an explanation, I could see that she knew a lot. Perhaps not everything, but definitely a good deal. I knew if I came here to study, I would learn more about it. After all, I did not have a job to occupy me. I could devote all my time to this, not just Saturday afternoons and one evening a week.

Before leaving, we saw Mr. Iskra again. He was still busy putting up that exhibition, but he stopped to talk to us. I said that I found everything terribly interesting and that I would like to learn more about it if he would take me on as a student. He had no doubt from the beginning what I was about to say, he seemed to sense rather quickly the center of my interest. He just said drily that if I really wanted to study with him, I could start any time I wanted. At that time I did not know that "teaching" was his major source of income.

Gertrud came regularly twice a week, Tuesday night from seven to nine and Saturday afternoon. I wanted to come on the same days, but if possible also on two other days during the week. It *was* possible and the very next week I started.

12

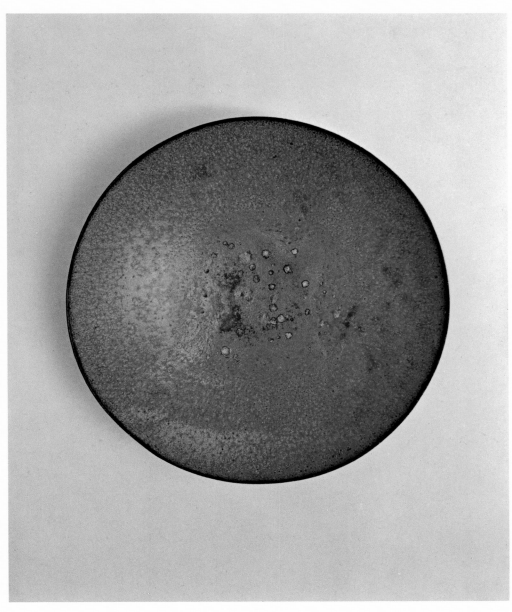

OLD TURQUOISE TRAY. 1941

"NOCTURNE" BOTTLE. 1961

This was an entirely novel sensation for me. Up to that time my only creative experience had been in designing textiles. There one begins by sketching on paper. Then one makes a more elaborate drawing and from this a technical drawing is made on which one indicates what materials, what colors, etc. should be used. After that, other people take over and produce what one had in mind.

My only other experience in art had been in music. In playing an instrument, you learn to master it, you perfect your technique, your musical comprehension. Then you study and practice. You work for weeks or months toward performing and after the performance is over, all that remains is what lingers in your memory. The best performance fades and you cannot rehear it. On the other hand, a bad performance is felt immediately and is remembered as such, but there is nothing left that you can work on, improve or make good. You must start all over from the beginning and even then you are not sure whether it will be better next time.

To work in clay, I soon found out, is quite different. To begin with, clay actually takes the form of three different materials. As long as clay is soft and plastic, it can be bent, pushed, squeezed, molded, cut. One can add more clay to it or take some away; one can roll it, one can tear it; one can draw on it by incising, and erase by rubbing one's fingers over it; one can impress into it both positive and negative designs. And always there is an immediate reaction, something one can see, evaluate, correct, if necessary. When clay begins to dry and to harden, it can still be bent to a degree, though not as easily as before. At this stage it can be carved. One can engrave in it or cut it. It can be joined together. But it has become a very different material from what it was when one

AZURE CYLINDRICAL VASE. 1961

started out. As the clay dries completely, it becomes hard. By then it has lost all its plasticity and one cannot bend it any more without breaking it. One can still sand it, shave or scratch it with a tool. At this point clay is brittle and very fragile.

I was very much intrigued with the many stages of clay and how each stage lends itself to a different treatment. It also intrigued me that one can work clay with just one's hands, without tools or implements, and produce something, slowly improving and changing as the work progresses, and in the end have something *lasting* as a result. I sensed clay as the miracle it really is. And strangely, after having worked with clay for about a week, I had completely forgotten that it is used to make "ceramics."

Mr. Iskra was a very "busy" man, though seldom seen around his students. When we needed instruction, we had to ask his assistant who showed me how to wedge clay, how to make coils and slabs, and how to cut, bend and join them. When it came to the wheel, his instruction was a little sketchy, but then at times the master himself would sit down and demonstrate. Such demonstrations were, of course, highlights and everybody would gather around the wheel to watch. Mr. Iskra's technique in throwing was just fabulous. His hands were very strong and sturdy, and with a sure grip he would center a big lump of clay. He used a piece of chamois to do this and often, even before he had quite finished centering, up went the clay, very fast and perfectly true-running. Then he put the chamois down, went over the pot once more with his hands, pulling it up and usually widening it a bit at the top. As the final touch he worked on the base with a small tool and his fingers, shaping the wet clay outward with a slight curve. This was his trade-

15

mark to which everybody referred with reverence as the "master's foot." Nobody knew exactly how he did it, it went so fast, and as soon as he had finished that part, his grey eyes would look up with that mischievous smile: "Now you try it if you can!"

At times he would continue to throw, making five or six pots exactly alike. Everybody looked on in awe and I, too, was impressed by his speed, skill and technique, though for some reason the forms he produced left me rather cold. His way of shaping his famous "master's foot" intrigued me, but I found it plump and heavy, unrelated to the form. Even though Gertrud's technique was hardly developed and could certainly not be compared to his, her way of throwing was infinitely more sensitive. The few pots she completed were graceful and elegant in form and even then remarkably thin. I still remember a small bowl she made the first year, simple in its patrician outline, beautifully curved into a base that was somewhat too narrow, yet still perfectly balanced in its proportions. That bowl had no resemblance to any ceramic I had known before–I loved that pot and Gertrud gave it to me.

I had been going to Mr. Iskra's workshop four times a week for about a year. The few pieces I produced were either sculptures or hand-built vessels. At the wheel, Gertrud's talent was so superior that I got somewhat discouraged about my own efforts. I did throw a few pots, but what really interested me most from the very beginning were those glazes, those pink and grey liquids one applied to the clay and which turned yellow, green or blue in the kiln.

I have always been curious. I wanted to know whether the glazes were made here in the workshop and how one made them. The assist-

16

APPLEGREEN BOTTLE. 1960

BLUE TIGER EYE BOWL. 1948

ant told me that most of them came from a factory in Czechoslovakia. "All we do here is mix them with water." "Can't one make them oneself?" "One probably could if one knew how." I wanted to know how.

The next time I saw Mr. Iskra, I told him that I was very interested in these glazes and that I would like to know more about them. Yes, I knew they came from Czechoslovakia, but could he tell me this: Here were pink or orange or grey liquids which would turn green or blue or yellow or even black after the firing. One could not tell by looking at them what color they would be; all one knew was what it said on the label. How does this change in color come about? What happens?

Mr. Iskra especially liked students who were interested and curious about things. It made him happy that I asked and he thought it was a good and valid question. "And you know," he said, "you hit right upon it, this is one of the great mysteries of ceramics!"

Unfortunately his answer did not quite satisfy my inborn sense of curiosity and I hoped, some day, to get a little more information.

There were a great many other things that made us unhappy with the set-up, not the least of them being the hour long streetcar ride to the workshop. So, one day, Gertrud and I sat down and figured the cost. There was the tuition we paid for our lessons, which of late consisted mainly in the privilege of using the workshop and the wheels. Then there were the charges for the clay, the glazes and the firing, a considerable extra expense, as well as the carfare. To all this the cost of the "Kaffeehaus" had to be added. Although there was no obvious connection between this typical Viennese institution and our making ceramics, its cost had to be figured as the price of spending our evenings together. It all added up to a considerable sum.

As we were both very serious about continuing this work and equally serious about being together, what could be more logical than finding a small studio. Some time previously, Gertrud had bought a potter's wheel which she installed in the bathroom of the apartment she occupied with her parents, not quite the ideal place for it.

Our financial computations led us to the conclusion that the rent for a small workshop should be within our budget. It was just a matter of finding one. We agreed that we needed no further instruction. It seemed to us that we knew everything there was to know, all we needed was a little practice and experience. This we could gain better if we devoted more time to work and less to travel. We put an ad in the paper, seeking a studio not too far from where we lived.

Before continuing, I would like to explain the local situation as it concerned us. Gertrud's office, just about 10 minutes walking distance from her home, was in an old building, diagonally opposite the apartment house where I lived at that time. Right across from it was the only "modern" building on this street, a six-story apartment house. It had an elevator and central heating, something quite unusual for Vienna in 1934. On the door of the building hung a sign: "Studio for Rent." We often walked by that door and always saw the sign, but paid little attention to it. We both were convinced that it could not possibly be for us. It would have been just too convenient.

We had quite a few answers to our ad which we followed up. There were huge workshops and tiny studios, some on the top floor of a walk-up, some down in the basement without daylight. Many of them were too far away or too expensive. We had set ourselves a limit of 60 schillings per month for the rent.

It was toward the end of a long winter and we felt discouraged. I had occasion to go skiing and left Vienna for a week in the mountains. Soon after my return, Gertrud and I walked home from a Philharmonic Concert late one afternoon, and again we passed that sign "Studio for Rent." We decided to inquire about it. After all, one could ask and look at it, even if it wasn't anything.

A pleasant young woman, the janitor's wife, answered the door bell. Surely, she would be glad to show us the studio. Up we went, all the way to the top floor – the elevator really worked. And then she opened the door.

"DUSK" BOWL. 1950

HERE was the most beautiful studio one could imagine, about thirty-five feet long and twenty wide, with a ceiling at least fourteen feet high, about half its area skylight. The entire north wall consisted of windows, starting about five feet from the floor and reaching up to the ceiling. The light was incredible, especially on entering from the rather dimly lit staircase. The warmth of the steam heat felt wonderful after the wintry street. A section of the main room was partitioned off by a six foot wall for privacy, and there was another small room to the right that could be used for storage. We were speechless, but finally managed to inquire about the rent. It rented for seventy schillings a month, plus about thirty schillings or so for the heat during the winter months. Our hearts sank. Sixty schillings was our very maximum and though we would have sacrificed heaven knows what in order to get it, we felt that this was beyond our reach.

Mrs. Papuschek was very nice about it and suggested we talk to the landlord, Mr. Spitzer, if we really liked it so well. After all, the place had been vacant for so long, perhaps he would let it go for less. Mr. Spitzer owned the hat factory in back of the building. Since this was a Saturday, nobody was there, and this meant waiting until Monday. The first time we had seen the sign was at least six weeks ago, but suddenly we were terribly afraid someone might rent the studio between now and Monday.

On Monday morning I knocked at the door of Mr. Spitzer's office.

20

TIGER EYE BOTTLE. 1954

"NOCTURNE" FOOTED BOWL. 1957

"I am interested in renting the studio." "Are you an artist?" "Yes, I work in clay, but we are just beginning. We understand the rent is seventy schillings; this is more than we can afford at this stage. Could you perhaps…" "Are you Jewish?" He interrupted me to ask this question. Oh, for God's sake, what has this to do with the rent, I thought. Of course, one should have been accustomed to this question; it was not unusual in Vienna at that time. "Yes, I am," I replied, expecting to hear that the studio had just been rented an hour ago. "You can rent it, if you want, for fifty-five a month plus whatever the heat is during the winter." I looked up in surprise and realized Mr. Spitzer was Jewish.

Gertrud's wheel was moved from her bathroom. We got some tables, a small kiln and built some shelves. Behind the partition we set up a primitive living area, a table, a few chairs and a couch, a book case and a few shelves for our favorite pots. To make tea, we had an electric hotplate and eventually we made our own tea set. One of the first visitors, having been compelled to stir his tea with a modelling tool, brought us three teaspoons on his second visit. We had lots of plants, mainly Philodendron, Epiphyllum, succulents and cacti which thrived in our studio, for not only was there a great deal of light, but the heat coming through the glass roof together with the moisture from clay and wet rags created near hothouse conditions, especially during the summer months.

Most of our time was spent in the big workroom, either at the wheel, or sculpting or at the kiln. We were on our own now and if we had imagined before that we knew everything one could learn, we soon found out differently.

The wheel we knew how to handle; all we needed was practice. But there was this monstrous kiln, what did one do with that? Neither of us had ever set a kiln before nor did we know at what temperature to fire it. I knew about pyrometric cones, but not which ones to use. We had bought some of the glazes from that factory in Czechoslovakia and, fortunately, the salesman gave us some information that proved helpful.

The first bisque-fire went off fairly well, only one piece blew up. We glazed all the other pieces, not knowing what would happen. Our knowledge was limited to what was printed on the labels. And then, with great trepidation, we fired the first glaze kiln, attentively watching the cones through the peephole for signs of bending. This would have indicated the desired temperature, but unfortunately the cones bent in the wrong direction and we could not observe them. We shut the kiln off and let it cool for a day. It was difficult to wait that long, the suspense was killing us. Finally, the next day–the kiln was still very hot–we opened it and there was complete disaster. Everything, but literally everything, was ruined. What should have been green, yellow or blue all looked quite similar, but none of these colors were apparent. Everything had turned out in different shades of brown. I could see that one should not rely on labels. Also, there were puddles of glaze on the kiln shelves. Only weeks later did I realize what had happened. The glazes had obviously been considerably overfired, they had run off the pots and what remained was not sufficient to give color to the terracotta of the clay.

At the bottom of the kiln there was, however, a happy surprise. One pot looked beautiful and interesting because of the overfiring. The glaze had formed a pattern of streaks which made the piece really fascinating, but the unfortunate part was that the glaze had run underneath the pot. It was solidly stuck to the shelf and in trying to pry it loose we broke it completely.

There we were, the work of many weeks a complete failure. My brother Paul had told me before: "You are crazy! People who want to achieve something go to school, they go to the Kunstgewerbeschule for four years, then they get a job to gain experience and then, perhaps, they may know something. With audacity alone one does not achieve anything. Not even pots!" I must say that neither of our families proved very encouraging.

Of course, Gertrud could not go to the Kunstgewerbeschule, she had her job with which she financed most of our enterprise. I had visited the Kunstgewerbeschule one day on a tour, but what I saw was not what I wanted to learn. It reminded me too much of "ceramics" again. But I loved clay. I just did not want to go to school and spoil that love. There had to be another way.

Gertrud continued to throw on the wheel. She could not be discouraged so easily and by now she was getting quite proficient. Throwing on the wheel is the fastest part of making ceramics and since she did not have much time at the studio, she concentrated on that part. As the studio was so close to her office, she often came during her lunch hour and she also sneaked over whenever her boss was away for any length of time. Evenings, right after work, she nearly always came and after a light supper, secured from the neighboring delicatessen store, owned by a man with the extraordinary name of Nachtnebel (Nightfog), we went to work, often until midnight.

Alas, I continued to ruin a great many pots with my unfortunate glaze experiments. By this time I had a small selection of manufactured glazes whose reaction I had come to know, and I had begun to inter-mix them, hoping to improve the colors. This, of course, created new problems. I was sure that in mixing black and white I would get grey, so it surprised me no end that I got green instead.

I had just about arrived at the first usable results from these glazes and their combinations when my old chemistry text from High School fell into my hands. There, on a little over half a page, was a chapter on "Pot-tery and Porcelain." The book was written by my chemistry teacher at the Realschule, a man by the name of Hugo Ludwig Fulda, whom I admired greatly. To me he was the best teacher who ever lived and a wonderful human being besides. I am still grateful to him for opening my eyes and mind to many subjects, in addition to chemistry.

That chapter on "Pottery and Porcelain" was not very extensive, but it was inspirational to me. It listed among other things some of the raw materials used in the manufacture of ceramic glazes. I found out where to buy these materials and was surprised that even the most ex-pensive of them cost only a small fraction of what we paid for com-mercial glazes. I was very excited about the prospect of making my own glazes, not to mention the savings this would entail.

Up to this time I had tried perhaps 150 of the manufactured glazes of which I used about twenty regularly. From these I had created eighty to ninety of my own combinations and was just getting to the point where I knew how to handle them, when, with great enthusiasm, I started out making and mixing "my own glazes." What followed now was a whole new series of disasters.

With about as much knowledge as the first potter on earth, I started to mix the materials I had bought. I mixed indiscriminately whatever came into my hands and, of course, the results were in keeping with my complete lack of knowledge. I finally decided not to ruin any more of Gertrud's pots, but made tiles on which I conducted my tests. Though I had no knowledge on which to base my experiments, I acted like a research scientist, numbered every tile carefully and kept a complete detailed record to which I could easily refer.

If the previous tests had been disastrous, these new experiments were devastating. What were intended to be glazes, were unmelted coatings that could be peeled off the clay. There were crusty surfaces that looked as if they had come out of the sea. Others had blisters, pockmarks, holes, craters. I kept all these tests and their record and tried to improve them. Gradually I found out the reaction of the various materials, and one day I finally achieved something that looked like a real glaze.

Somehow, however, more instinctively than consciously, I was attracted to the faults and the mistakes and to the surfaces that did not quite look like glazes. For some reason I felt that they expressed much more the medium itself. At that time I had no opinion of my own, I thought a ceramic was clay and glaze, and one used the kiln and its heat to combine the two. The realization that a ceramic is much more elemental, and that in a true ceramic the fire is an integral part of the medium, came much later.

The first experimental tiles began to intrigue me. I tried a new series of experiments in the other direction. Instead of working toward a smooth surface, I tried to increase the blisters, make the pockmarks, the holes and craters more pronounced, get away from those bright,

GREY-WHITE BOWL. 1952

shiny colors. I used some of these new concoctions on Gertrud's pots and the results were strange indeed. They certainly did not look like any of the ceramics one could see in stores.

About a year had passed since we had rented the studio and by this time we had placed a few pieces in some shops. We made progress financially, too, for now we could cover our expenses. The pots we sold at that time were unsigned, with only our initials impressed on the bottom of each piece: ⏍ The initials stood for Trude (short for Gertrud) Amon–Otto Natzler. All pots we made in Vienna were stamped with these initials, except a few we made for a shop called Haus & Garten which were stamped H & G.

This brings to mind a rather amusing incident. Altogether, three shops in Vienna bought our work, and one day I set out to conquer a fourth and most exclusive one. It was owned by the architectural firm

26

of Frank & Wlach and displayed the very finest of crafts and furniture. The shop was run by the wives of these two architects. I mustered up enough courage to go in and show some of the pots we had made most recently. Klari Wlach was in charge of this department. After the first customary reaction to me and my yet unopened bag: "We don't handle many ceramics and we really don't need any now," I tried to make it clear that I just wanted her to look at them, it would not take more than five minutes of her time. She was very charming and I was young and timid, and I tried to put on my best smile which finally convinced her that I could not highpressure her into any purchases. She looked at the pots and was rather surprised at what she saw. She noticed the forms in their austere outlines, but she also was quite aware of the surfaces, which were not the surfaces of the ceramics of the Wiener Werkstätte. She wanted to buy some of these pots, but then she looked and hesitated. She had discovered the ⌶⌒ stamp on the bottom. She said we should make pots similar to these, but make them specifically for the shop and stamp them with H & G.

We did not like to make things to order, partly because we were not certain of the outcome, and I would much rather have sold her the pieces I had with me instead of carrying them back again. But her request also irked me. I said that we would certainly do what she wanted, but it was my strong belief that in ten or fifteen years the initials ⌶⌒ would be at least as renowned as H & G. If she thought anything of my remark, she did not tell me, she just insisted on her request.

About twenty-five years later, Klari Wlach visited us in Los Angeles. We both recalled this episode and laughed heartily. She then looked at our latest pots and suddenly there were tears running down her cheeks.

FLAME RED VASE. 1960

[IV]

NOT TOO MANY PEOPLE visited us at our studio in Vienna. We did
not encourage it, for we wanted our solitude. We wanted to work alone
and be together. We loved our work and each other and it was at this
early beginning that we started to collaborate in nearly all our work.
We did not compete, but on the contrary concentrated on different
facets of the medium. We inspired each other and taught each other.
And, of course, we criticized. We could be our severest critics as well
as our staunchest admirers. What we produced were not so much ceramics as works of love. It was love for the medium we worked in and
each piece was meant to satisfy only our very own aesthetic concept.

At times we tried to enter work in group exhibitions. Mostly it was
rejected. By now, in working with clay, we were oblivious to the fact
that it is used to make "ceramics," and, unfortunately, ceramics exhibitions were exhibitions of ceramics.

In 1937 we tried again. This time it was the World Exposition in Paris
and work could be submitted to a jury for an exhibition sponsored by
the Austrian Government. We entered ten pieces, the maximum one
could submit, and, to our surprise, five of them were accepted. What
triumph! We decided to devote part of our summer vacation to a trip
to Paris. There, in the Austrian Pavillion in a glass case were our five
pots among perhaps a hundred others. One of them had a red dot, a

29

sign that it was sold, and we were elated. Our "success" in Paris was followed by another. We had our first one-man-exhibition at a gallery, the Gallerie Würthle in Vienna, and saw our first review of this exhibition in the art section of one of Vienna's leading papers.

Barely four years had passed since we first touched clay. Things seemed to be looking up for us, except for the dark clouds that gathered on the political horizon of Central Europe. In 1938 those clouds grew more menacing. Almost daily there were riots and demonstrations, and the Austrian Government decided to call a plebiscite for the 13th of March. By late February and early March the demonstrations became more frequent and more violent. One could feel what was coming and it was nothing good. I had written to a cousin of mine in California, the only person I knew in the United States, inquiring in general whether one could go to that faraway country. I wrote him what we were doing and asked him what he thought our chances were for pursuing our work. I mailed that letter on the 10th of March.

In the morning of the 11th I was at the studio as usual. There was an official envelope in the mail. On the outside it was rubber-stamped "Jeder Oesterreicher stimmt mit Ja!", the official government slogan "Every Austrian votes Yes." Inside was a form letter from the Ministry of Education, informing us that our work had been awarded a Silver Medal at the World Exposition in Paris. I called Gertrud at the office, something I seldom did. She would not believe me and thought I was joking.

In the evening of the same day the Germans marched into Austria. Two days later Hitler arrived and annexed the country. Austria had ceased to exist.

30

We knew we could not remain and the next five months were spent in obtaining passports, immigration papers to the United States and passage on a boat. It was a formidable task and in between we tried to do some work at the studio. It was rather half-hearted. Our only aim was to get all the papers together and to leave the country. On the 15th of September we left Vienna where we had spent the first thirty years of our lives.

OLD TURQUOISE MASSIVE BOWL. 1958

IVORY CELADON BOTTLE. 1962

About Gertrud's Throwing and About Form

TO WATCH Gertrud's throwing is the sensual-aesthetic experience that one has in the presence of anyone who is a master of his medium. There is the graceful movement of her hands, exerting complete positive control over the clay from the first firm grip during the centering, leading into a progressively lighter touch while shaping the general outline. There is never any sign of excessive force or strained effort, it all is a continuous, completely natural, controlled motion, gradually diminishing in force, until that very last "breathing" of her fingertips, producing that last sensitive flare of the lip to complete and balance a form. By that time the walls of the vessel often are eggshell-thin and it seems quite incomprehensible that the soft clay can support all that weight.

Gertrud's hands, seeming to belong to a dancer, are most expressive in their movement. Yet unlike a dance movement that is transitory in nature, a most tangible motion remains: The Form of a Pot.

After watching Gertrud throw, one looks at a pot through different eyes, and one's relationship to it is no longer the same. One begins really to understand Form, to feel it. One realizes for the first time that this form, in its ideal proportions looking as natural as if it had grown from the soil, is the expression of human hands and mind – the mood of a moment caught and retained in the soft clay. The clay will harden, the fire will give it permanence, and a fleeting moment of time will have been translated into form and preserved.

33

Form is, of course, the most important part of a pot. It is the primary, the most basic component, from which everything else will develop. It can be a most static as well as a most dynamic factor. Form is not just the shape of a pot. It is the manner in which that shape develops, how it originates, how it ends. It is the arrangement of the curves, its outline; it is the porportions as they apply to a particular shape.

Our approach to form is purist. Form should be natural, free of distortions (excepting those inherent in the medium and those the medium may produce through its own forces). We believe in the absence of the artificial ornament or ornamentation for the sake of "enhancing" the form. (Again excepting those ornaments which the medium itself may impart through its own natural forces.)

The form of a pot is the main part of its spiritual substance. Its outline, its proportions and balance, the fingermarks impressed on its wall, are the simple statement of its creator, spontaneous and as personal as his handwriting. It is also unique as to the hour or the minute it was made. The same pot does not happen twice.

A pot is four-dimensional: One can think of it as sculpture in three dimensions with the important inside added as the fourth. The inside, while not identical with the outline of a pot, must relate to it. The inside of a closed form such as a teardrop, or bottle, has all the fingermarks, all the evenness or unevenness of a hand-thrown pot, yet this inside remains hidden from the eye and the touch. Only when the pot breaks will it reveal itself, like a tree that reveals much of the marvelous structure of its growth only in death and decay.

Proportions are an essential part of the form. They are the relation

34

DARK ROSE BOWL. 1961

SANG AND GREYGREEN TEARDROP BOTTLE.   1962

of the diameter of a pot to its height, the relation of both the height and the width to the base, the arrangement of the curves relative to each other on a specific form.

It is easy to talk, in the abstract, about proportions and their relation to a given basic form; but we still have to bear in mind the character of the medium which, by its own inherent behavior, may destroy the most ideally conceived proportions. Any conscious consideration of form will have to take this into account.

In saying this, I am thinking of the metamorphosis clay undergoes when it transforms from softness (the stage at which it is "thrown" and the main outline of the form is created), to leather-hardness (the stage when in many cases the base is formed by cutting) and finally, after drying, to complete hardness; and again of the transformation clay undergoes in the firing which hardens it even more, yet not before it may have undergone a softening period during the highest heat of the fire. In all these instances clay shrinks and the shrinkage will be in directions dictated by the form, influencing and at times distorting it. In addition, the force of gravity may come into play during that short softening period in the heat of the firing. These are the forces inherent in the medium which can and will influence the final form after it has been created by the potter.

There are as many different forms as there are pots, though there will always be specific ones that may have, more than all others, a special meaning to an individual potter. He will elaborate on them, concentrate on them, do them in hundreds of different variations, trying and searching for that which is most elusive—absolute perfection. In

35

Gertrud's case, there are four basic forms on which she lavishes this concentration.

The Round Bowl, lifting itself up from a narrow, perfectly integrated base, changing into a progressively convex curve and ending with a slight suggestion of turning back into itself. The visual center of gravity will be in the center of the pot.

The Bowl with a Flaring Lip may develop at its start like a round bowl, but then turns outward to form the lip, as if it were the ending balance for the curve it originates at the base. There is an airiness to this form, it seems to move as if floating in space, and the visual center of gravity lies in the uppermost part of the pot.

The Teardrop Bottle in its hundreds of variations widens quickly after lifting from its base. The form then ascends slowly upward with a slight curve, as if turning into itself, only to change direction faintly just before ending; at times it will do so with a distinct flaring outward. The visual center of gravity remains close to the base, and the outline, even after reaching the top of the form, seems to flow back into it.

The Double-curved Form, regardless whether it is a bowl or a bottle. Depending on the shape, the visual center of gravity can be either in the upper or in the lower portion of the pot. This form is most elusive as to the arrangements of its curves and proportions. In its ideal development it gives the impression of expanding and contracting motion, as if breathing.

It is Gertrud's contention that the basic form, important as it is, does not make the pot. Rather it is the manner in which the form develops. Her instinctive critical judgment is very keen and may impell her to destroy a pot she has just finished because of a curve not completely balanced, or a base a fraction too wide or too narrow. It is her feeling that form, regardless of shape and proportions – as long as the proportions are meaningful in relation to the shape – has to be continuous. Good form is not contained in itself. To be continuous, it has to flow outside its containment. Good form is unending, its outline will continue into its environment and return in an imaginary line to the point of its origin in an unbroken, never-ending flow.

BLUE-TINGE CELADON BOWL. 1951

The Appreciation of a Pot : Form and Fire

A pot seems a fragile thing while, at the same time, it is one of the most durable objects man can make. Fragility is, of course, one of the characteristics that make it even more precious. Handled with the care a good pot deserves, it will last indefinitely; it will be destroyed only when force is used. We know that our earliest history has been pieced together from pots or fragments of pots. Many of them, thousands of years old, have been unearthed in perfect condition. Metal objects equally old have long since corroded, wood and fabrics have decayed, and even stone has deteriorated to a degree. The colors in paintings have faded or darkened, but those in a fragile pot have remained the same. Even fire, though it may affect the pot, will not destroy it.

The hand-thrown pot is something that happens at the spur of the moment, and as it happens in a matter of minutes, it reflects the mood of that moment. The pot is formed without tools, entirely by hand, and the soft clay retains the fingermarks of its maker. In no other art is there such an immediacy, such personal, close contact. There is the brush between the painter and his canvas, the chisel between the sculptor and his stone, not to mention art where the machine or hordes of people are involved in its execution.

When you hold a pot in your hands, when you go over its walls with your fingers, you feel the hands of the potter, his fingermarks, his touch. You may not know who he was or what he looked like, but, handling

PLUM "NOCTURNE" BOTTLE. 1963

GREY CELADON BOWL. 1949

the pot, be it hundreds or thousands of years old, you can still feel the imprint of his hands. It is this fact about a pot that makes it so endearing, so very personal. It makes the physical handling of a pot such an important part of its appreciation, as important as its visual impact and at times even more so.

The emotional creative force of a human being gave form to a pot and imparted its very personal touch during the mood of the moment. The creation of form is but the first, though most important step. It provides the spiritual content–the most basic "ingredient" in any art. Yet it is still only a small part of what a pot really represents.

There is another creative human force involved, more gradual in developing. Intellectually conceived, it is the material composition of the pot, its physical body, that which represents the ceramic medium. It is the earthy-molten surface skin as it relates to the form of the pot.

The ceramic medium is Earth, Water and Fire. A meaningful ceramic exploits all three of these elements. In various expressions any of the three may receive more emphasis than the others.

In creating the ceramic form only two of the elements come into play: Earth and Water. Yet the third must be kept in mind for the form to be meaningful. Earth, Water and Fire are the physical substance of a pot. Its spiritual substance becomes visible and tangible as Form and Fire.

Fire is a "tool" as well as a part of the medium. As the first, its forces will combine all substances used into a whole: as the second, its force will relate to the form of the pot.

When I speak of fire, I don't mean just heat. Heat alone can be employed to produce a pot, but the pot will be sterile and sexless, just as pure heat is sterile and sexless. The fire I am speaking of is heat plus all the physical, elemental factors of fire, the raw, open flame, its force in shooting up, the draft it produces, the accompanying smoke and ashes. They all combine, controlled or uncontrolled, to create the pot we want to create.

The form of the pot will dictate how the fire should be used, whether controlled or wild. Control will be attempted to relate the fire to the form – flames, drafts, etc. can be increased or decreased at will – still at best it will be only partial control, a joint effort of the intellect and the elemental force of a natural occurrence.

The natural forces of fire exert influence upon any form in two directions: *Up* move the flame, the smoke and the forced draft, and *down* move the melting glaze, unburned particles and settling ashes.

Just as the forces of fire exert influence on the form, so will the form determine the path of the flame, the draft, the smoke, the ashes. The form will determine the movement of the glaze and its performance in the fire. There is a complete interrelation and interdependence between the two. The conduct of the fire is planned to make this interrelation harmonious or dissonant. The cycle is infinite, the interrelation of Form and Fire total.

Looking at the pot and comprehending this interrelation of Form and Fire – that subtle interchange of the emotional human force with the intellectually controlled uncontrolled elemental force – one's eye will see more and one's mind will have a keener appreciation of an art object, small enough to hold in one's hand, that contains, in all its fragility, the physical and spiritual forces of the universe.

40

About the Clay

The clay body we use in our work is thoroughly adjusted to our needs. We compound it by using two California clays from the Alberhill region as a base. To improve both the workability of the plastic clay and the firing capacity, we add several other ingredients. Though we have used this basic clay since about 1939, the final formulation was a development over a number of years, with the last minor changes made in 1948.

Great care is taken in the exact formulation of the clay, as it influences the character of a pot as much as anything that is used in its making. The outcome of the glaze, its color and texture after firing, will depend to a large degree on the clay underneath. Clay and glaze are going to unite to form a whole; they are equally important and we like to show the clay through the glaze. We do not use the glaze to hide the clay, but it always remains at least partially visible as the physical base of the pot. For this reason, the color of the clay is important to us.

In view of Gertrud's throwing, which produces vessels whose walls are frequently one or two millimeters thin, a careful preparation is imperative. The mechanical process of preparing our clay is a drawn-out affair. We start by weighing the individual ingredients, then mix them with an excess amount of water. After thorough mixing and a few hours of agitation, we let this slip soak for at least three to four weeks. After this soaking period, it is briefly agitated again, larger particles of clay are broken up, impurities above a certain size are eliminated, and a complete blending of the batch is effected.

After the clay slip has been allowed to stand for another several weeks, the clay will have settled and much of the excess water can be syphoned off. The slip is much thicker now and is laid out on plaster bats. Within a day or two the plaster will have absorbed enough water so that the clay will have reached its working consistency. The whole process takes a minimum of six weeks, though frequently several months. Once the clay has reached its working consistency, it is removed from the plaster bats and stored for further aging.

We prefer to use red firing clay for aesthetic reasons only. Throughout this collection the same red clay body is used (with minor variations before 1948), except for the two pots D465 and K092 which are made from different (experimental) clay bodies.

Due to its high iron content, the color of the clay is a warm terracotta-red after oxidation firing. In a reducing fire the color will turn dark brown or even completely black as the red ferric oxide is reduced to the black ferrous oxide.

The conduct of the bisque fire will also exert considerable influence on the color and the general character of certain glazes. In our case, the bisque is fired below the maturing range of the clay in order to preserve a certain degree of porosity which facilitates the application of the glaze.

CAT'S EYE TRAY. 1954

CAT'S EYE TEARDROP BOTTLE. 1966

About the Glazes

All glazes in this collection were developed since our arrival in California, though undoubtedly some of them have their origin in early experiments I conducted in Vienna. Several materials were new to us and responsible for the development of new ideas. Following are the main categories of our glazes as well as their characteristics, technical information and the year when a particular idea was first developed. Other data, such as color derivation, firing technique, etc. are provided in the catalogue section and are listed with each individual object.

"Pompeian" Glazes : 1939. These are glazes with fairly high lead content, thickly applied in several layers. Many of them show obvious deviations from the customary glaze surface, displaying pockmarks, blisters and shrivelled patterns with the glaze flowing viscously in heavy folds. Like most of the glazes of that period, they are completely opaque.

[985 2603 4434]

"Lava" Glazes : 1940. There are three distinct groups of variations : Lava Glazes, Flowing Lava Glazes and Lavastone Glazes. They are either semi-lead glazes or pure alkaline. The lava-like surface is achieved by addition of a Titanium-Silicon Carbide combination to the basic glaze. The application is always thick, in several layers. In the flowing lava glazes, a light-melting overflow is used of either a related glaze or one quite different in composition. The lavastone glazes are characterized by their rough, porous looking texture.   [3819]

"Reduction" Glazes: 1942. For the sake of simplicity, we are using the term "Reduction Glaze" consistently in this catalogue, even though the more correct designation should be "reduction-fired glaze."

Many of these glazes were composed specifically as such, others have been used as ordinary oxidation-fired glazes as well. I shall at this point briefly outline the principle and objective of the process. Oxygen is eliminated from the kiln by burning organic matter inside the muffle while the ceramics are being fired. We repeat this process at strategic intervals during the firing cycle. The purpose is to cause color changes in the clay and glazes through the withdrawal of oxygen. Depending on the method of reduction and the material composition of the reducing agent, there can be other physical side effects in addition to the color transmutation of the glaze. Smoke and flame marks will be indelibly inscribed in the finished pot.

Though the first reduction experiments were begun in 1942, conscious exploitation of all reduction effects did not take place until about 1947. Results achieved by us before that time were frequently purely accidental. Some of the more striking side effects of reduction are described below.

Iridescence: 1942. Iridescence occurs when reduction is continued into the cooling cycle to such a degree that some of the metallic compounds of the glaze are reduced to the elementary metal. Such metal will then be colloidally suspended in the glaze and cause the iridescence. If reduction is continued too far into the cooling, the iridescence may turn into a vulgar metallic luster. In our early experiments we frequently, though involuntarily, arrived at such pieces which we used to destroy.

44

GREY EARTH "CRATER" BOWL. 1959

Later on we refired such objects to eliminate the luster. A faint iridescence, especially in glazes containing copper or iron, can be quite a becoming attribute.

[5795 9294 A308 E426 G012 J254 J512 L400 L507 M959 N690]

Melt Fissures: 1944. The first pieces showing this phenomenon were accidental. There were occasional pieces showing melt fissures as early as 1942. It took however well over a year after these first "accidents" to find an explanation for them. They are the result of a cooling draft, causing the surface skin of the glaze to solidify during the fire, tearing it and exposing glaze matter from underneath. A detailed study of the technology of each glaze, mainly its behavior during the firing, was necessary to control this occurrence.

[4749 (8020) 9294 (9565) A112 A308 (C934) F062 F186
(J254) K998 L385 L507 M870 N355 (N690) N802]

Smoke and Fire Marks: 1949. That which seems to occur so naturally has become the most difficult to exploit and control. Smoke traces appear on many pieces as early as 1949 and, purely by accident, even before. Many of the early pieces show draft-induced wrinkles (elephant skin) in addition to smoke effects. The really violent fire marks, such as in the applegreen bottle K998, were not exploited until about 1960. An even more violent reaction is achieved on the Cat's Eye Teardrop N802 in 1966. The effect fascinates me and I am further exploring its technique at the present time.

[A112 B674 F186 J512 (*flame marks*) K998 L385 N802]

"Crater" Glazes: 1948. These are essentially similar in composition though not in outward appearance to the earlier "Pompeian" glazes. In contrast to them, they are technically harder, requiring a higher firing temperature, and the application of the glaze is heavier. A later combination with the "Lava" glazes achieves an interesting, even rougher surface. The pronounced deep craters in these glazes develop during the firing process and are caused by emission of gases through the glaze surface. Nearly all crater glazes are one-fire glazes (oxidation).

[9500 K230 L009]

"Crystalline" Glazes: 1956. With the exception of a crystalline gunmetal glaze containing an over-saturation of copper and an "aventurine" glaze made from iron – both dating back to early 1940 – serious work on crystalline glazes did not begin until 1956. None of the better developed crystalline glazes, such as K274 in this collection, were made before 1959. A variety of different materials were used to induce crystallization. The principle, simply stated, is always the same, to produce an oversaturated solution during the firing which, upon partial cooling of the still liquid glaze, will form crystals of the dissolved solids. Upon complete cooling, these crystals will appear retained as such in a solidified solution. The chief difficulty here was to find a suitable vehicle in a glaze that would stand a long span of liquefaction without running off the vertical planes of a pot. A precisely controlled cooling cycle is essential. Most of our crystalline glazes are transparent or semi-transparent.   [J254 K274 (K662) L094 L507 M870 (M959)]

"Multi-Fire" Glazes: 1963. This category includes only multi-fired oxidation glazes. Experimentation was begun much earlier, but the first conscious exploitation of the possibilities of the MF technique did not start until 1963. At the present state of this collection there is only one example of this type of glaze represented. [N671]

In general this category comprises our hare's fur glazes, some crystallization glazes and glazes where translucency and depth of color is achieved by this method. Another reason for employing this technique is the utilization of certain glaze compositions which technically could not be applied in the required thickness without partial prefiring.

Scholars and others interested in additional data may be surprised to learn that all 56 pieces in this collection are derived from nine different basic glazes. Following are listed the individual objects as they relate to the various glazes.

Glaze I:	985	2603	4434					
II:	3819							
III:	5795	6757	A067	A308	A313	B666	C336	C934	D465
	E426	E988	F062	J512	L959			
IV:	5621	7103	9294	B674	F075	F186	K998	M508	N802
V:	9500	D615	K230	L009 (*in combination with Glaze II*)				
VI:	2097	K092	L297	N671				
VII:	K662							
VIII:	2420	4749	9565	A112	L385			
IX:	8020	8474	G012	G945	H525	J254	K274	L094	L266
	L400	L507	M870	M959	N355	N690		

The Roman numerals indicate the basic glazes. The variations in color and texture are achieved by various additives to the glaze.

GREY CELADON BOWL. 1948

Frequently, different firing temperatures and atmospheric changes
during the firing cycle are the cause of color and texture variation. How
extensive such variations in a single glaze can be is seen by comparing
the individual pieces in each of the following five groups, each group
representing one single glaze.

Group A	Group B	Group C	Group D	Group E
5621	7103	9565	F075	L266
B674	9294	A112	N802	L400
K998	F186	L385		

Even though the individual pieces in each group vary widely in appearance, the glaze is of exactly the same chemical composition. The
differences in color and texture are achieved by varying methods of
reduction, different firing cycles and temperatures, and the use of a
variety of reducing agents. The method of firing is described with each
pot in the catalog section. There are, of course, infinitely more possible variations for each individual glaze.

49

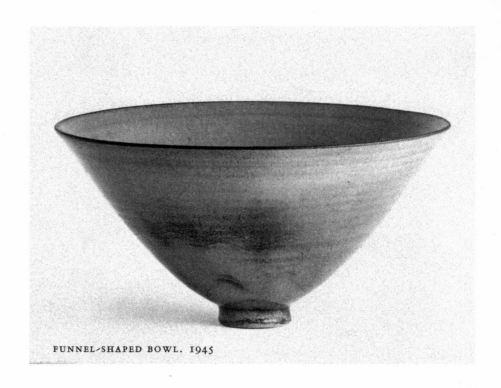

FUNNEL-SHAPED BOWL. 1945

The assembling of the collection began in 1961, when about thirty pots were acquired as a nucleus. As it was Mrs. Sperry's intention to present the collection in its entirety to one institution, she chose to limit the scale of the individual pieces. Considering space limitations at most museums, she felt that it would be easier to house the collection under one roof if larger pots were not included.

For the purpose of easy reference and authentication, the ceramics in the Sperry Collection are identified by their original numbers. The pieces—as all our ceramics—are signed NATZLER, *the only exceptions being 985 and 2097. These two are signed* G & O NATZLER, *as are most pieces made before the year 1942.*

GREEN AND BROWN CRYSTALLINE BOTTLE. 1959

ORANGE-RED "POMPEIAN" BOWL. 1944

The information in the catalog section is taken from records and notes we have kept since 1939. After our arrival in the United States every piece was recorded, with the exception of the first 200 or 300 pieces produced in early 1939. These records are always kept up to date and entries are made in chronological order as soon as pieces are completed. Each pot is given a consecutive number when taken out of the kiln after the final firing. The record for each object indicates the approximate form of the pot, its dimensions and the glaze. (A complete, detailed record for each reduction fire is kept separately.) Numerals 1-10,000 indicate the ceramics produced between 1939 and 1948. Later pieces were identified with a one-letter-three-digit combination. The following table indicates the dates:

1939	1 - 361	1949	A081 - B240	1959	K121 - K640
1940	362 - 1286	1950	B241 - C320	1960	K641 - L240
1941	1287 - 2100	1951	C321 - D320	1961	L241 - L840
1942	2101 - 2877	1952	D321 - E160	1962	L841 - M560
1943	2878 - 4158	1953	E161 - E1000	1963	M561 - M1000
1944	4159 - 5420	1954	F001 - F840	1964	N001 - N400
1945	5421 - 6500	1955	F841 - G840	1965	N401 - N720
1946	6501 - 7820	1956	G841 - H360	1966	N721 - N920
1947	7821 - 9020	1957	H361 - J280	1967	N921 -
1948	9021 - A080	1958	J281 - K120		

CATALOG OF THE COLLECTION

985 BOWL [1940]
Diameter 17 cm Height 7 cm Green-Brown "Pompeian" Glaze

A heavy lead glaze, thickly applied in several layers. The "Pompeian" glazes developed from some of the first accidents I encountered in trying to produce a ceramic glaze. The surface of the glaze is pockmarked, caused by bubbles forming during the firing process. A very precise firing cycle is essential in developing this glaze. Oxidation fired at approx. 1000°c.

2097 TRAY [1941]
Diameter 12 cm Height 2.5 cm Old Turquoise Glaze

This is one of the earliest examples in this particular type of glaze and, incidentally, one of the best. In this glaze, too, use is made of the tiny "explosions" caused by bursting bubbles during the firing process. The color is derived from copper with tin as an opacifier in a pure alkaline base. The glaze contains a considerable amount of natural cryolite, a sodium-aluminum-fluoride. Oxidation fired at approx. 1000°c.

2420 BOWL WITH FLARING LIP [1942]
Diameter 19 cm Height 6.5 cm "Sang," and Green Copper Reduction Glaze

The remarkable characteristics of this bowl are its near-perfect proportions—the well integrated somewhat narrow base, counter-balanced by a slight flare of the lip. The glaze is one of my very first attempts of reduction, stemming from the 5th Reduction Fire. It was an experimental fire to explore the possibilities resulting from lack of oxygen. The color is derived from copper, with tin used as opacifier and a trace of manganese as catalyst. Two fires: Oxidation and Reduction.

2603 BOWL [1942]
Diameter 18 cm Height 8.5 cm "Pompeian Earth" Glaze

This is one of the best examples of the Pompeian glazes—a high lead content glaze thickly applied. There is a heavy flow of glaze partially covering the base. The color is derived from a combination of iron and manganese with tin and zinc used as opacifiers. Oxidation fired at approx. 1000°c.

54

985

2603

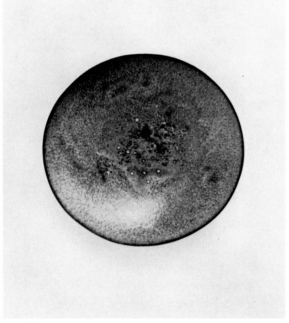

2097

2420

3819 BOWL [1943]
Diameter 21.5 cm   Height 8.75 cm   Turquoise-Grey Flowing "Lava" Glaze

A very hard grey crusty lava glaze with bright turquoise overflow. The stark earthiness of the "Grey Lava" is complemented by the heavy viscous overflow, contrasting the elements of "Earth and Water" as part of the ceramic medium. The grey of the lava is produced from silicon carbide, the color of the blue overflow is derived from copper. Oxidation fired at approx. $1000°c.$ to $1050°c.$

4434 BOWL [1944]
Diameter 13.25 cm   Height 6.5 cm   Orange-Red "Pompeian" Glaze

One of the early examples of the Pompeian Reds. As in all Pompeian glazes it is high in lead content. Due to its heavy application – characteristic of this group – the movement of this glaze during the firing process is arrested in heavy folds, a striking example of the physical effects of the fire retained in the pot. The bright orange-red color is derived from uranium. Oxidation fired at approx. $1000°-1020°c.$

4749 ROUND BOWL [1944]
Diameter 14.5 cm   Height 9.5 cm   Copper Reduction Glaze, Melt Fissures

The deep rose colored copper reduction glaze with a slight undertone of green shows the typical tracery pattern of melt fissures caused by forced-draft cooling.

Although the pattern is extremely well developed it was purely accidental – for at the time the piece was made the cause of it was still an enigma, occurring at some and not at other firings. The color is derived from a combination of tin, copper and manganese. Reduction Fire No. 10 at $1000°c.$ (No previous oxidation fire.)

5621 FUNNEL-SHAPED BOWL [1945]
Diameter 18.5 cm   Height 10 cm   Grey-Yellow Reduction Glaze

The character of this bowl is typical of that period; an austere form completely balanced on its narrow base, underlining an ascending motion. The color is derived from copper. The piece was first fired in a regular oxidation glaze fire and subsequently reduction fired at $1010°c.$ (Reduction Fire No. 17.)

3819

5621

4434

4749

5795 BOWL [1945]

Diameter 14 cm   Height 5 cm   Oxblood Glaze with Iridescence

This is an alkaline glaze, the color derived from copper. The bowl has a slight metallic lustre and a very faint pattern of melt fissures. Despite its early date, barely three years after my first experiments in reduction, it remains the best example of this glaze. Due to heavy application thick drops form around the base. Two fires: Oxidation at approx. 1070°c., Reduction at 1010°c. (Reduction Fire No. 18.)

6757 ROUND BOWL [1946]

Diameter 11 cm   Height 7.5 cm   "Sang" and Blue Reduction Glaze

In composition this is the same glaze as 5795. The outside of the piece shows a bright red as the result of reduction, while the inside is blue, almost the oxidation color of the glaze. A good example of the "copper story" on one pot. Examination through a magnifying glass reveals the whole story of the reduction fire effects. Two fires: Oxidation and Reduction. (Reduction Fire No. 24.)

7103 ROUND BOWL [1946]

Diameter 12 cm   Height 6.5 cm   "Tiger Eye" Reduction Glaze

This is one of the first "Tiger Eyes." Like many of the pots with tiger eye glazes the texture is glossy on the outside and matted on the inside, caused by ash deposits from smoke during the reduction fire. The color is derived from antimony in a glaze with high lead content. Two fires: Oxidation at approx. 1070°c., Reduction at 1030°c. (Reduction Fire No. 27.)

8020 SMALL BOWL [1947]

Diameter 11.5 cm   Height 3 cm   Green and "Sang" Reduction Glaze

This glaze, of the peachbloom family, shows a faint pattern of melt fissures. It is one example from a series of experiments in which the color is derived from a combination of iron, titanium and copper in a semi-alkaline base. Two fires: Oxidation at approx. 1070°c., Reduction at 1030°c. (Reduction Fire No. 37.)

5795

7103

6757

8020

8474 SMALL BOWL [1947]

Diameter 11 cm   Height 3 cm   Celadon Reduction Glaze

The glaze is quite similar to the one on 8020, except that the color is derived from a combination of iron and manganese in a semi-alkaline base. It is one of the rare examples of this glaze because of smoke traces and a mutation of the color towards green. A controlled flow of the glaze at the base, and spiral finger-marks from throwing partly visible, add to its attraction. Two fires: Oxidation at approx. 1070°c., Reduction at 1040°c. (Reduction Fire No. 40.)

9294 BOWL [1948]

Diameter 14 cm (top 12.5 cm)   Height 9 cm   Blue "Tiger Eye" Reduction Glaze

This glaze shows a very pronounced pattern of melt fissures and elephant skin texture. It is basically the same glaze as the tiger eye bowl 7103, but received different treatment in the reduction fire. The effect of this very explosive fire is vividly retained on the glaze in the strong pattern of melt fissures and abrupt color changes. The glaze is faintly iridescent. Two fires: Oxidation at approx. 1070°c., Reduction at 1000°c. (Reduction Fire No. 42.)

9500 BOWL [1948]

Diameter 18 cm   Height 8 cm   Peagreen "Crater" Glaze

This is a very heavy lead glaze in thick application with a pronounced earthy appearance. The craters form through gas emissions during the firing process. It is a later development of this "earthy" type of glaze, dating back to our very beginnings. The color is derived from a combination of copper and antimony. Oxidation fired only, at approx. 1070°c.

9565 SMALL FOOTED BOWL WITH FLARING LIP [1948]

Diameter 11.5 cm   Height 5.5 cm   Grey Celadon Reduction Glaze

This bowl with its slightly flaring lip has nearly ideal proportions. The inside of the piece shows imbedded carbon particles from excessive smoke, rarely retained in such a clearly defined pattern. On the outside there is a tracery of melt fissures. The glaze is semi-alkaline with color derived from manganese. One fire: Reduction. (Reduction Fire No. 43.)

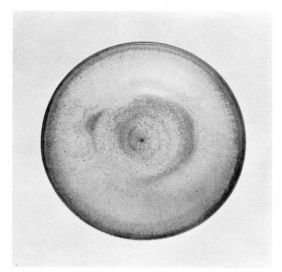

8474

9500

9294

9565

A067 SMALL BOWL [1948]

Diameter 11.5 cm   Height 4 cm   Viscous Purplish Grey Celadon Glaze

The glaze is very heavily applied and allowed to flow naturally in the fire, forming drops and leaving part of the base uncovered. This strangely complements and enhances the sensitive curve of the base of the bowl. The color is derived from a combination of iron and manganese in a pure alkaline glaze. Two fires: Oxidation at approx. 1070°c., Reduction at 1000°c. (Reduction Fire No. 44.)

A112 SMALL BOWL [1949]

Diameter 10 cm   Height 4.5 cm   Grey Celadon Glaze with Melt Fissures

The outside of the bowl was only partly glazed, with the glaze allowed to perform "naturally" in the fire, thus leaving part of the base uncovered. The pronounced melt fissures, showing smoke effects and an elephant skin typical of this type of glaze, highlight the form of the bowl. In every respect this unassuming small pot is one of the most beautiful examples of the natural integration of form and fire. The color of the glaze is derived from manganese in a semi-alkaline base. One fire: Reduction. (Reduction Fire No. 45.)

A308 SMALL BOWL [1949]

Diameter 10.5 cm   Height 5.5 cm   Golden Peach Blossom Glaze with Melt Fissures

In addition to the subtle pattern of melt fissures the glaze shows an iridescent lustre. The color is derived from a very small amount of copper in combination with iron in a semi-alkaline base. Two fires: Oxidation at approx. 1070°c., Reduction at 1000°c. (Reduction Fire No. 47.)

A313 BOWL [1949]

Diameter 13.5 cm   Height 5 cm   Olive Celadon Reduction Glaze

The color in this glaze is derived from a combination of tin and iron with a minute addition of cobalt in a semi-alkaline base. Two fires: Oxidation and Reduction. (Reduction Fire No. 47.)

A067

A308

A112

A313

B666 BOWL [1950]
Diameter 9 cm   Height 8.5 cm   Peach Blossom Reduction Glaze

This deep rose-colored glaze has a slight metallic lustre. The extremely thin shell shows pronounced fingermarks from throwing. The color is derived from a very small amount of copper in combination with iron in a pure alkaline base. Two fires: Oxidation and Reduction. (Reduction Fire No. 50.)

B674 BOWL [1950]
Diameter 11.5 cm   Height 7 cm   "Dusk" Reduction Glaze

The outside of this bowl is remarkable for the effect of the smoke and the greyish color it imparts to the glaze. The slight red blush is easily understandable since the glaze contains copper as its coloring ingredient. It is puzzling, though, how some black marks, seemingly fingerprints, were retained through the fire. This is one of the very few of our pots showing such fingerprints. Two fires: Oxidation and Reduction. (Reduction Fire No. 50.)

C336 BOWL WITH FLARING LIP [1951]
Diameter 14 cm   Height 9 cm   Oxblood Glaze with Smoke Traces

This is one of the sensitively curved forms with barely a suggestion of a lip, quite typical of Gertrud's throwing. The glaze is one of the later oxbloods which, in contrast to the earlier examples, has a much finer texture. The color is derived from copper in a semi-alkaline base. Two fires: Oxidation and Reduction. (Reduction Fire No. 52.)

C934 BOWL WITH FLARING LIP [1951]
Diameter 10 cm   Height 7.5 cm   Blue-Tinge Celadon Glaze
with a faint pattern of Melt Fissures

One of the best blue-tinged celadons ever to leave our kiln. It is a highly evasive color derived from iron with a small addition of cobalt in a semi-alkaline base. The thin walled pot with its slightly flaring lip encourages the natural run-off of the glaze, and the resulting dark rim enhances both glaze and shape. Two fires: Oxidation and Reduction. (Reduction Fire No. 54.)

B 666

C 336

B 674

C 934

D465 BOWL [1952]

Diameter 21 cm Height 6 cm Heavy Viscous Pale Yellow Glaze on Black Clay

The glaze shows pin holes and bubbles caused by gas emissions during the firing. It covers the outside only partially and is allowed to flow freely in the fire. Oxidation fire at approx. 1080°c.

D615 BOWL [1952]

Diameter 14.5 cm Height 5 cm Grey-White Mat Glaze, Black Red-Rimmed Spots

Despite its early date this pot was acquired for the collection only in 1967. It is a freak stemming from a series of experiments I conducted in the early 50s. The black spots are produced from small bits of metallic copper added to the glaze; the red rims are caused by reduction. Two fires: Oxidation and Reduction. (Reduction Fire No. 56.)

E426 FOOTED BOWL [1953]

Diameter 14.5 cm Height 4 cm "Sang" and Blue Reduction Glaze, Faint Melt Fissures

An austere form, it is one of the most sensitively thrown small pots in this collection. The peach blossom type glaze shows extremely subtle variations of color, mutating from blue into red. The accidental effects of the reduction fire are especially noticeable on the outside with its red blush and slight metallic lustre. The color is derived from a small amount of copper in a semi-alkaline base. Two fires: Oxidation and Reduction. (Reduction Fire No. 60.)

E988 BOWL [1953]

Diameter 11.5 cm Height 6.5 cm Lavender Blue Reduction Glaze

The elephant skin texture on this glaze is due to drafts during the reduction fire. This is a forerunner of a glaze I was to perfect in 1961, the "Mariposa" Reduction Glaze. The color is derived from iron and cobalt. Two fires: Oxidation and Reduction. (Reduction Fire No. 61.)

E426

D465

D615

E988

F062 BOWL [1954]

Diameter 15.5 cm   Height 5 cm   Mossgreen and "Sang" Reduction Glaze, Melt Fissures

The effects of excessive smoke during reduction, caused by green plant material, are visible. The glaze is remarkable for its very pronounced pattern of melt fissures and its color mutations. The color is derived from a combination of titanium, antimony, iron and copper in a semi-alkaline base. Two fires: Oxidation at approx. 1070°c., Reduction at 1015°c. (Reduction Fire No. 62.)

F075 TRAY [1954]

Diameter 14.5 cm   Height 3.5 cm   "Cat's Eye" Reduction Glaze

The Cat's Eye is in composition closely related to the Tiger Eye Glaze, except that its color is greener. This particularly light example shows the effects of excessive smoke, caused by introduction of green plant material during the reduction fire. The color is derived from a combination of titanium, antimony and cobalt in a lead glaze. Two fires: Oxidation and Reduction. (Reduction Fire No. 63.)

F186 BOTTLE [1954]

Diameter 15 cm (top 2.5 cm)   Height 15 cm   "Tiger Eye" Reduction Glaze

This is a medium dark tiger eye that shows sharply pronounced melt fissures and elephant skin texture. Excessive smoke as well as ash deposits caused an abrasive matting of the glaze. The color is derived from titanium and antimony in a lead glaze. Two fires: Oxidation and Reduction. (Reduction Fire No. 65.)

G012 SMALL DOUBLE-CURVED BOTTLE [1955]

Diameter 11 cm (top 1.5 cm)   Height 15 cm   Peachbloom Reduction Glaze

The well proportioned form of this bottle enhances the natural flow of the glaze along its walls. This is one of the rare instances in which a related glaze – an iron titanium combination in a semi-alkaline base – was used as the first coat. The color itself is derived from a second coat containing copper in a pure alkaline glaze. Two fires: Oxidation and Reduction. (Reduction Fire No. 71.)

F062

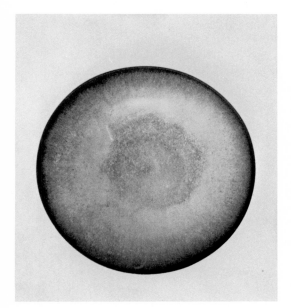

F075

F186

G012

G945 ROUND BOWL [1956]
Diameter 11 cm   Height 4 cm   Blue Reduction Glaze

One in a series of cobalt reduction glazes which led to the "mariposa" glazes. There is some faint crystallization in this glaze. Two fires: Oxidation and Reduction. (Reduction Fire No. 78.)

H525 FOOTED BOWL [1957]
Diameter 10 cm   Height 12.5 cm   "Nocturne" Reduction Glaze

This is an extremely subtle semi-transparent greyish brown glaze with purple overtones. The color is derived from a combination of titanium and vanadium in a lead-alkaline base. Two fires: Oxidation and Reduction. (Reduction Fire No. 84.)

J254 BOWL [1957]
Diameter 15 cm   Height 6 cm   "Nocturne" Reduction Glaze

The inside of this bowl has a pronounced melt fissure straight across it. Both outside and inside show the transition of color from green to "sang," the outside predominantly "sang" with slight iridescence. The glaze has a crystalline structure throughout and is one of very many variations. The colors are derived from a titanium-copper combination in a semi-alkaline base. Two fires: Oxidation and Reduction. (Reduction Fire No. 87.)

J512 BOWL [1958]
Diameter 11.5 cm   Height 5.5 cm   Peach Blossom Reduction Glaze

This is one of the best examples in this particular glaze. In contrast to other peach blossom glazes it has a rather high copper content. The outside of the bowl shows typical flame marks from the reduction fire. The color is obtained from a combination of copper and titanium in a semi-alkaline base. Two fires: Oxidation and Reduction. (Reduction Fire No. 88.)

G945

J512

J254

H525

K092 BOWL [1958]
Diameter 13 cm   Height 7 cm   Old Turquoise Mat Glaze

This is one of the few massive pieces we produced at that time. A different clay body with grog content was used. The turquoise glaze is produced with copper and tin in a pure alkaline base with fluoric acid content. Oxidation fired.

K230 BOWL [1959]
Diameter 12.5 cm   Height 9.5 cm   Grey Earth "Crater" Glaze

A nearly cylindrical bowl with a heavy feldsparic lead glaze, white with black craters. The glaze shows the effects of separation (crawling) during the firing process. The colors are produced from a tin-manganese-iron-cobalt combination in a semi-alkaline glaze. Oxidation fired.

K274 BOTTLE WITH CUPPED TOP [1959]
Diameter 9 cm (top 6 cm)   Height 23 cm   Green and Brown Glaze
with Crystal Formations

This is a rare variation of a semi-transparent green crystalline glaze. The color is derived from a combination of manganese and copper in a semi-alkaline base. Oxidation fired.

K662 VASE WITH FLARING TOP [1960]
Diameter 8 cm (top 5 cm)   Height 21 cm   Flame Red Mat Glaze

This is an orange-brown-black glaze showing tiny "explosions" on its surface. The color is derived from uranium in a heavy lead glaze. Oxidation fired.

K 092

K 274

K 230

K 662

K998 BOTTLE WITH WIDENING TOP [1960]
Diameter 13.5 cm (top 4 cm)   Height 22.5 cm   Applegreen
Reduction Glaze with Fire Marks and Melt Fissures

The fire marks are caused by the raw open flame and the draft it created. The color of the glaze is derived from a combination of copper, antimony and titanium. Two fires: Oxidation and Reduction (in limited reducing atmosphere).

L009 BOTTLE [1960]
Diameter 11 cm (top 3 cm)   Height 38 cm   Bluish Grey "Crater" Glaze

This is an extremely heavy glaze, quite rough in texture, with deep black craters. It is the result of a combination of a normal crater glaze and one of the "lava-stones." The color is derived from a combination of manganese, cobalt and copper in a heavy feldsparic lead base. Oxidation fired.

L094 VASE [1960]
Diameter 9 cm   Height 16.5 cm   Blue Crystalline Glaze

This glaze is rather similar in character to that of K274. The color is derived from a combination of cobalt and copper. Oxidation fired.

L266 CYLINDRICAL VASE [1961]
Diameter 7 cm   Height 16 cm   Azure Blue Glossy Glaze

The glaze has a tendency to flow off the edges of a vessel when properly fired, exposing the clay color underneath, thus accentuating the rim of the pot. The color is derived from cobalt in a semi-alkaline base. Oxidation fired.

K998

L094

L009

L266

L 297 BOWL [1961]

Diameter 11.5 cm   Height 8 cm   Dark Rose Copper Reduction Glaze

The copper reduction glaze shows not only the roughness of a pure alkaline glaze with high fluoric acid content, but also the effects of the fire and smoke during reduction. The color is derived from copper. Two fires: Oxidation and Reduction. (Reduction Fire No. 92.)

L 385 TEARDROP BOTTLE [1961]

Diameter 12.5 cm (top 2 cm)   Height 24 cm   Grey Celadon Reduction Glaze

I believe this to be one of the best proportioned teardrops we made. The glaze is a grey celadon, produced with tin and manganese in a high alkaline base. It shows a pattern of carbon deposits, emphasizing the form, and traceries of melt fissures. The natural flow of the glaze covers the base of the pot only partially, exposing some of the clay. One fire: Reduction. (Reduction Fire No. 94.)

L 400 SLENDER TEARDROP BOTTLE WITH FLARING TOP [1961]

Diameter 10 cm (top 4 cm)   Height 28 cm   Green "Mariposa" Reduction Glaze

This is one of the exceptional pots in this particular glaze. The blue blush on one side is caused by reduction of titanium. Usually the glaze shows a wholly different blue from re-oxidized cobalt. There is a faint pattern of melt fissures in parts of the surface. The color is derived from a cobalt-titanium combination in a high alkaline base. Three fires: One Oxidation and two Reduction. (Reduction Fire No. 95.)

L 507 BOTTLE [1961]

Diameter 10.5 cm (top 5 cm)   Height 15.5 cm   "Nocturne" Reduction Glaze

One in a series of Nocturne glazes. This is a copper glaze with crystalline formations and a bright red blush on one side, caused by uneven reduction. Some melt fissures enliven the surface. Two fires: Oxidation and Reduction. (Reduction Fire No. 96.)

76

L297

L400

L385

L507

L959 BOTTLE [1962]

Diameter 11.25 cm (top 3 cm) Height 13.5 cm Ivory Celadon Reduction Glaze

The round bottle form lends itself well to the unevenly applied glaze which is allowed to perform freely by its natural flow during the fire. The color is derived from an antimony-titanium-iron combination in a high alkaline base. Two fires: Oxidation and Reduction. (Reduction Fire No. 100.)

M508 TEARDROP BOTTLE WITH GROOVED LIP [1962]

Diameter 11.5 cm (top 2 cm) Height 21.75 cm "Sang" and Greygreen Reduction Glaze

The color is derived from a titanium-antimony-copper combination in a high lead base. The striking effects of very uneven reduction manifest themselves in abrupt color changes. Two fires: Oxidation and Reduction. (Reduction Fire No. 104.)

M870 VASE [1963]

Diameter 18 cm Height 22.5 cm "Nocturne" Reduction Glaze

The glaze on this piece is unlike any other in its peculiar, almost violent color variations. The colors mutate from a deep olive to a magenta-red, there are crystal formations in the glaze and a weird pattern of melt fissures. The colors are derived from copper and titanium in a semi-alkaline base. Two fires: Oxidation and Reduction. (Reduction Fire No. 109.)

M959 SPHERICAL BOTTLE [1963]

Diameter 17 cm (top 2 cm) Height 16.25 cm Plum "Nocturne" Reduction Glaze

This is a faintly crystalline glaze of deep plum color. There are well defined bright red areas from partial reduction, as well as a slight metallic lustre. The colors are derived from a copper-cobalt-titanium combination in a semi-alkaline base. Two fires: Oxidation and Reduction. (Reduction Fire No. 111.)

78

L 959

M 870

M 508

M 959

N355 BOTTLE [1964]

Diameter 8.5 cm (top 1.5 cm)   Height 24.5 cm   Blue "Nocturne" Reduction Glaze

The deep blue glaze shows a faint pattern of melt fissures. There is a luminous glow in this semi-translucent glaze, the color of which is derived from cobalt with slight additions of titanium and vanadium. The base is semi-alkaline. Two fires: Oxidation and Reduction. (Reduction Fire No. 115.)

N671 SQUAT BOTTLE [1965]

Diameter 17 cm (top 2 cm)   Height 9.5 cm   Emerald-silverblack Glaze

The deep emerald colored glaze on this pot is multi-fired. It has a high copper content in a pure alkaline base. The colors are derived from a tin-copper combination; the translucency is the result of the two fires which also cause the partial crystallization of the copper. Two fires, both Oxidizing.

N690 BOTTLE [1965]

Diameter 14.5 cm (top 1.5 cm)   Height 16.5 cm   "Sang Nocturne" Reduction Glaze

The combination of the severe form of this bottle with the deep sang nocturne glaze gives it a strange and mysterious character. This is heightened by the iridescence of the glaze and a faint pattern of melt fissures. The colors and the character of the glaze are derived from a combination of copper, titanium and vanadium in a semi-alkaline base. Two fires: Oxidation and Reduction. (Reduction Fire No. 122.)

N802 TEARDROP BOTTLE [1966]

Diameter 8.5 cm (top 1.25 cm)   Height 17.5 cm
Dark "Cat's Eye" Reduction Glaze with Craters

The cat's eye glaze in this pot shows crater eruptions and violent melt fissures. More than ever before, use is made of the physical effects of the raw flame and the accompanying drafts, causing unburned particles to imbed themselves in the glaze. The result is a surface with open blisters, wrinkles and melt fissures on one side and completely smooth on the other. Two fires: Oxidation and Reduction. (Reduction Fire No. 125.)

N 355

N 690

N 671

N 802